Chiff Chaff and Chickpea
In Search of Sounds

First published 2008

Published by Youth Music
1 America Street, London SE1 ONE
www.youthmusic.org.uk
Registered charity number 1075032

Story text © Miriam Moss 2008
Illustrations © Emil Dacanay and Sian Rance 2008
Activities text © Alison Blunt 2008
Music and lyrics © Malcolm Bruce 2008
Design D.R. ink
Edited by Laura Atkins

With thanks to Cassy, Elliot, Esmie, Imogen, Morwenna and Finn, Maya, Sam and Stella, Theo, Woody and Pete.

Printed and bound in Belgium
by Proost International Book Production
ISBN 978-0-9558293-0-7

Chiff Chaff and Chickpea
In Search of Sounds

Written by Miriam Moss

Illustrated by Emil Dacanay and Sian Rance

Musical activities by Alison Blunt

Music and lyrics by Malcolm Bruce

Chiff Chaff and Chickpea
sat high in their tree.
"Does everyone cheep like me?"
said Chickpea.
"Oh no!" said Chiff Chaff,
"but now we're awake,
let's visit some friends,
hear the sounds that they make!"

- How do you move when you wake up?
- How does a tree move on a windy day?
- ▶ ② Can you wake up like Chickpea in his nest?

- How do birds sound? Make 'bird chat' with voices and fingers. Try high and low, long and short, fast and slow sounds.
- ▶ ② Can you hum and sing with the birds?

- ▶ ② Can you play along with soft sounds?
- Can you make music for the rustling leaves?
- Take turns playing 'bird chat' with your instruments.

- ▶ ③ Listen and sing along with *"Oh little bird"* while sitting in your 'nest'.

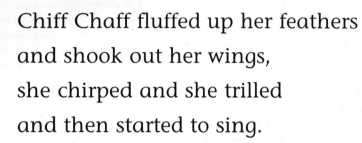

Chiff Chaff fluffed up her feathers
and shook out her wings,
she chirped and she trilled
and then started to sing.

With a whoosh and a whirr
and a one, two, **three** –
Chiff Chaff and Chickpea
flew out of their tree.

- Using hands or your whole body, shake out your 'wings' and fly like a bird!
- ▶ ④ Explore the music by moving high and low, fast and slow.

- Make flying music.
- ▶ ④ Play the beat exploring different kinds of sounds.

- Can you count "**1, 2, 3**"? Can you count and play three sounds?

- Try saying "with a **WHOOSH** and a **WHIRR** and a **ONE**, two, **THREE**" using different voices, actions and sounds.

They swooped down, glided and delicately –
landed in the branches of a banyan tree!

There in the river with a **sploosh** and a **trump**,
swaying and swinging and raising her trunk,
stood elephant washing, and, bending her knees
she bowed, then she sang and she danced with Chickpea.

"Oh thank you!" cried Chickpea.

"I liked THAT a LOT!

But we've more friends to see –
so must fly from this spot!"

- How does an elephant move its trunk? Can you walk with elephant steps?
- ▶ ⑤ Can you kneel and bow like this elephant? How would she dance and move her trunk?

- How high and low can you go?
  - Lowering arm slide voice down.
  - Raising arm slide voice up.

- "With a **SPLOOSH** and a **TRUMP**" – can you play the **BEAT** of the **WORDS**?
- ▶ ⑤ Can you play and sing the *"BIG AND STRONG"* pattern? You could try this together all through the song!

- Take turns matching elephant steps with instrument sounds.
- ▶ ⑤ Play along!

They swooped down, glided and delicately –
landed in the branches of a date palm tree!

There in the sand with a swish and a plod
with bells on his harness a camel trod.
He offered them apricots, almonds and dates.
"We've travelled so far! **Let's celebrate!**"

- Can you move like a camel?
- ▶ ⑥ Can you find matching movements for the bell sounds? Can you dance with swinging arms and hips?

- How many bells can you count in the picture? Can you play this number of sounds?
- Can you whisper and play quietly for the camels plodding far away? Try getting gradually louder – the camels have arrived! Gradually change back to whispering – they're going away again!

- Can you share your instruments like the camel sharing his food?
- "AP-RI-COTS"
  "AL-MONDS"
  "DATES"
  Can you play these words with your instruments?
- ▶ ⑥ Play along!

They swooped down, glided and delicately – landed in the branches of a baobab tree!

Cheetah's feet ran fast with a **drumming sound**,
then got slower and slower till she flopped to the ground.
Grasshopper sang with a scurr, scurr, scurr,
while under the baobab the cheetah purrrrrred.

▶ ⑦ Can you make a running dance?

▶ ⑧ How do you move when you are tired? Can you dance with these movements?

▶ ⑦ Chant or sing along.

• Can you make "**SCURR**" and "**PURRRRRR**" sounds? Try short, long, quiet and loud sounds.

• Using your voice, can you swap between "**SCURR**" and "**PURRRRRR**" sounds to make a pattern?

• Can you use instruments to make the cheetah and grasshopper sounds?

• Play and direct each other: **FAST! SLOW! STOP! GO! QUIET! LOUD!** What other directions can you give?

▶ ⑦ Play along!

▶ ⑧ What kind of sounds match this music best?

They swooped down, glided and delicately –
landed in the branches of a coconut tree!

A nut hit the ground with a **THUD** and a **CRACK!**
They broke it open with a Tap! Tap! Tap!
Then they dived in the water to hear dolphin click,
and raced round with him – but he was far too quick!

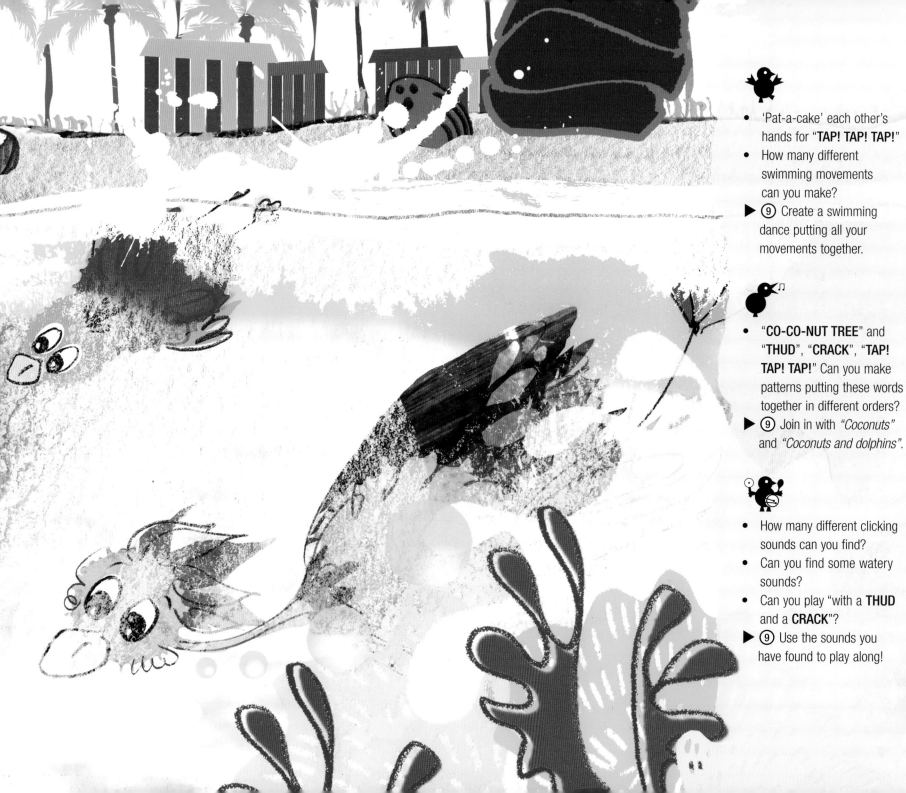

- 'Pat-a-cake' each other's hands for "**TAP! TAP! TAP!**"
- How many different swimming movements can you make?
- ▶ ⑨ Create a swimming dance putting all your movements together.

- "**CO-CO-NUT TREE**" and "**THUD**", "**CRACK**", "**TAP! TAP! TAP!**" Can you make patterns putting these words together in different orders?
- ▶ ⑨ Join in with *"Coconuts"* and *"Coconuts and dolphins"*.

- How many different clicking sounds can you find?
- Can you find some watery sounds?
- Can you play "with a **THUD** and a **CRACK**"?
- ▶ ⑨ Use the sounds you have found to play along!

They swooped down, glided and delicately – landed in the branches of a monkey nut tree!

Far away the howler monkeys went
"Hou, hou, hou,"
then came leaping and swinging
as monkeys do.
But CLAP! went the thunder
and they all scampered off
while the rain pattered down
with a Plip! Plip! Plosh!

- Can you swing like a monkey?
- Flick your fingers for the falling rain – "Plip! Plip! Plosh!"
- ▶ ⑩ Do your own swinging monkey dance!

- What other songs or chants about rain or monkeys do you know?
- ▶ ⑪ Sing along, adding your own rain words.

- Make rainstorm music. Try starting very quiet… gradually get louder… stop with a clap!
- ▶ ⑪ Can you play along, making rainy sounds?

- ▶ ⑪ Can you move to *"DRIP DROP, SPLISH SPLASH, DRIP DROP DRIP DROP"*? Join in with your voice and instruments.

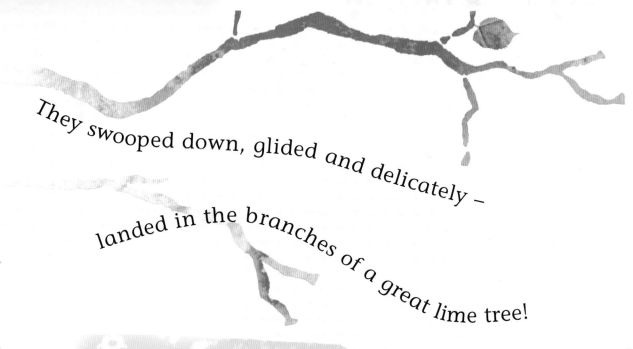

They swooped down, glided and delicately –

landed in the branches of a great lime tree!

As the snowflakes fell on the street below,
a high voice squeaked, "I'm a bat, you know!"
She was there on the branch hanging upside down,
with umbrella wings folded, soft and brown.

- How do you move when you are cold?
- Can you move upside down like a bat?
- ▶ ⑫ How would the bat dance?

- Raising your eyebrows, can you have high squeaky conversations?

- Can you make 'snowflake sounds'?
- Can you make squeaky sounds?
- Can you swap between snowflake and squeaky sounds to make a pattern?
- ▶ ⑫ Tap, shake or scrape a 'bat beat'.

- ▶ ⑫ Add your own squeaky bat sounds!

They swooped down, glided and delicately –
landed in bamboo as tall as a tree!

There hid shy panda,
Chickpea took a peek.
"He's moving very **slowly**,
is he playing hide and seek?"

"Yes," said Chiff Chaff **softly**.
"How many can you see?"
"Two," **whispered** Chickpea,
"and that baby makes three!"

- How slowly can you move? Can you use the drum to hide and surprise each other?
- ▶ ⑬ Listen to the sticks and bells. Can you rock or step to this pattern?

- How many animals are there in the picture?
- ▶ ⑬ Can you join in with humming or clicking sounds?

- Together, play 'Guess the Sound'. Turn your back while your partner plays an instrument. Did you hear the maracas, the drum or the cymbal?
- ▶ ⑬ Play along. Can you match the bell and stick patterns?

They swooped down, glided and delicately –
landed in the branches of a eucalyptus tree!

Kangaroo bounced past,
going hop hop hop!

"Hello!" called Chickpea.

"Won't you stop, stop, stop?"

"Sure guys," said Kanga.

"And if you can bounce too –
we can play a game of leapfrog, I'll jump over you!"

- Can you jump? Can you hop? Take turns to say "**STOP**".
- ▶ ⑭ Can you jump slowly and quickly to match the music?

- Move and chant:
  'I can jump, jump, jump!'
  'I can rock, rock, rock!'
  'I can slide, slide, slide!'
  Find other ways to move and chant.

- ▶ ⑭ Sing along!

- Can you beat **HOP** HOP **HOP**, **HOP** HOP **HOP** together? Try using different speeds. Take turns to make a "**STOP**" sign.
- ▶ ⑭ Play along with the beat.
- ▶ ⑭ Can you match the wooden Tapping Sticks sound?

"It's late now," said Chiff Chaff
and shook out her wings...
But Chickpea said, "It's my turn now!"
And HE started to SING!

With a whoosh and a whirr
and a one, two, **three** –
Chickpea led Chiff Chaff
right out of the tree.

- Using hands or your whole body, can you shake out your 'wings' and fly like a bird?

▶ ⑮ What flying sounds can you make with your voice?

- Can you count "1, 2, 3"? Can you find and play three different sounds?

- Can you sing and play your favourite song? Do you have a dance for it?
- Play 'follow-my-leader' using voices, actions and sounds.

They swooped down, glided and delicately – landed in the branches of their own oak tree!

"Goodness me!" cried Chiff Chaff,
"I'm very impressed.
You've brought us safely back
to our lovely warm nest!
We've met lots of friends
who don't all go 'cheep'.
Now I'm feeling quite tired –
would you sing ME to sleep?"

Proudly Chickpea sang about
the purrs and the clicks,
the squeaks, bells and dancing,
and panda's hiding tricks.

- How does a bird 'swoop down'? Can you move your arms or whole body to 'fly' down and land in your 'nest'?
- How would Chickpea feel and move after his adventures?

▶ ⑯ Sing along with *"Oh little bird"*.

▶ ⑯ What sounds and words have you been hearing and making?

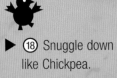

- Count the instruments back into the drum 'nest' ready for their next adventure.

⑰ Whisper or sing each line of Chickpea's lullaby after your hear it.

⑱ Snuggle down like Chickpea.

Then he snuggled down
and whispered, "I liked today.
Can we see more friends tomorrow?"
And Chiff Chaff whispered, "Okay."